Analogies
Grades 6-8

MW00396259

Table of Contents

Introduction

Analogies build critical thinking and reasoning skills that are important in everyday learning as well as for standardized testing. Students can begin to learn the relationships shown in analogies by working with shape and picture analogies that compare familiar items. (The Grade 2–3 book in this series introduces shape and picture analogies.) Students can then progress to more difficult analogies that involve multiple choice and finally to supplying words from their own experience to complete analogies. The thinking skills required to complete analogies are creative and higher level, encouraging students to think "out of the box." This kind of reasoning will strengthen their thinking abilities across the curriculum and serve them throughout their lives in all kinds of activities.

ORGANIZATION AND USE

This book is divided into four units: Completing Analogies from a Word Box, Completing Multiple Choice Analogies (One Word), Completing Multiple Choice Analogies (Word Pairs), and Supplying Words to Complete Analogies. The exercises progress from simplest to most difficult, and may be most effective when used in order; however, teachers may use any lesson at any time. Each two-page lesson has a sample exercise and an explanation of how the analogy should be read and completed. Units Two, Three, and Four are curriculum area-oriented to help integrate analogies across the curriculum.

At the end of each lesson is a short "Analogy-Wiz" exercise indicated by the "Wizard" icon. These exercises help stretch students' thinking and prepare them for the types of analogies that are to come in the book. There is also a one-page "Fun with Analogies" lesson at the end of each of the first three units.

Three assessments at the beginning of the book can be used as pre-tests or post-tests, or at any time a teacher wishes to gauge students' understanding of the lessons. The tests cover Completing Analogies from a Word Box, Completing Multiple Choice Analogies, and Supplying Words to Complete Analogies.

On page 3 is an introduction to analogies, which teachers should go over with their students before beginning. The introduction describes what an analogy is, how it looks, and how it should be read. For grades six through eight, all analogies are written using the symbols ":" and "::," which represent "is to" and "as" respectively. If teachers wish to introduce analogies using words rather than symbols, the grade 4–5 book may be used as practice before moving on to this book.

The answer key gives answers as well as relationships to help teachers explain how to think through each analogy.

ADDITIONAL NOTES

Some Analogy-Wiz activities suggest partnering with a classmate or sharing with the class. Additional paper will be required in many cases.

Activities may be completed individually in class or as homework, in small groups or centers, or as a class. It is suggested that the teacher go over the examples and their solutions before having students work independently. As the vocabulary spans three grade levels and challenges thinking across the curriculum, students will benefit from access to a standard dictionary. At times, the direction lines will suggest the use of other reference materials as well.

Analogies can be challenging, and they can also be fun. They are, in a sense, puzzles and brain teasers, and students' attitudes toward analogies can be positively influenced by treating the exercises this way. Encourage students to be creative, and be sure to keep an open mind. At times, there will be more than one right answer. If a student has a new answer, ask for an explanation. Through the explanation, the student will more clearly see the error of his or her thinking, or the teacher will see an interesting new solution!

Name _____ Date _____

Introduction to Analogies

An **analogy** is a way of comparing things.
An analogy has two parts, joined by the word **AS**.

This is a picture analogy:

 is to **AS** is to

This analogy compares how the **fish** and **bowl** are like the **bird** and **cage**. A goldfish lives in a fish bowl. A parakeet lives in a bird cage.

This is a word analogy:
green is to grass **AS** blue is to sky

This analogy compares how **green** and **grass** are like **blue** and the **sky**. Green is the color of grass. Blue is the color of the sky.

Read this word analogy. Which word from the box completes the analogy?

dog is to puppy **AS** cat is to _____

baby	kitten	meow

 Think: A **puppy** is a baby **dog**. Which word in the word box is the same to a **cat** as the puppy is to a dog?

Answer: A kitten is a baby cat, so **kitten** is the correct choice to complete the analogy.

An analogy can have symbols instead of words. It can look like this:
dog : bark :: cat : meow   : means **is to**   :: means **AS**

Now try these. Darken the circle by your choice.

leaves : tree :: trees : _____
    Ⓐ bark   Ⓑ trunk   Ⓒ forest

hat : head :: tie : _____
    Ⓐ knot   Ⓑ neck   Ⓒ silk

mom : dad :: sister : _____
    Ⓐ brother   Ⓑ uncle   Ⓒ girl

drop : break :: fall : _____
    Ⓐ down   Ⓑ injure   Ⓒ jump

Name _____   Date _____

Using a Word Box to Complete Analogies

(**Directions**) These analogies are antonyms, synonyms, homophones, or rhymes. Write one of these choices on the "Type of Analogy" line. Then, write the word you choose from the box to complete each analogy.

fryer	skill	priest	mustard	dessert	follow	perish	distant

1. correct : mistaken :: near : _____

   Type of Analogy _____

2. knight : night :: friar : _____

   Type of Analogy _____

3. delete : complete :: cherish : _____

   Type of Analogy _____

4. career : profession :: talent : _____

   Type of Analogy _____

5. never : always :: lead : _____

   Type of Analogy _____

(**Directions**) These analogies compare parts of a whole or a group, or cause and effect. Write one of these choices on the "Type of Analogy" line. Then, write the word you choose from the box to complete each analogy.

travel	galaxy	light	organs	desserts	deceive	shiver	stars

6. Earth : planets :: Milky Way : _____

   Type of Analogy _____

7. fan : breeze :: candle : _____

   Type of Analogy _____

8. sight : senses :: heart : _____

   Type of Analogy _____

9. paperclip : office supplies :: brownies : _____

   Type of Analogy _____

10. heat : sweat :: cold : _____

    Type of Analogy _____

(GO ON ⇨)

Assessment: Completing Analogies from a Word Box
Analogies 6–8, SV 6908-6

Using a Word Box to Complete Analogies

(Directions) These analogies describe the uses or characteristics of things. Write <u>use</u> or
<u>characteristic</u> on the "Type of Analogy" line. Then, write the word you choose from the box to complete
each analogy.

tool	identifying	science	taste	protect	relax	parch	mouth
dehydrate	temperature	pound	white	play	clear	silky	shine

11. bulb : illuminate :: light : _____

Type of Analogy _____

12. chisel : chip :: hammer : _____

Type of Analogy _____

13. blanket : warm :: game : _____

Type of Analogy _____

14. tidal pool : brackish :: spring water : _____

Type of Analogy _____

15. gravel : abrasive :: powder : _____

Type of Analogy _____

16. teeth : chew :: tongue : _____

Type of Analogy _____

17. scratch : harm :: varnish : _____

Type of Analogy _____

18. compass : direction :: thermometer : _____

Type of Analogy _____

19. water : hydrate :: heat : _____

Type of Analogy _____

20. rain : moisten :: sun : _____

Type of Analogy _____

21. office : work :: hammock : _____

Type of Analogy _____

22. carbon : dating :: DNA : _____

Type of Analogy _____

Multiple Choice Analogies

Directions For numbers 1–5, choose the word that best completes each analogy. Darken the circle by the word you choose. Tell why the analogy works or what it is comparing.

1. globe : sphere :: block : ?   Ⓐ square   Ⓑ cube   Ⓒ toy

2. sun : burn :: ozone : ?   Ⓐ melt   Ⓑ protect   Ⓒ layer

3. china : fragile :: leather : ?   Ⓐ brown   Ⓑ tough   Ⓒ shoes

4. infant : helpless :: teen : ?   Ⓐ able   Ⓑ old   Ⓒ parent

5. abrasion : pain :: ointment : ?   Ⓐ gooey   Ⓑ spread   Ⓒ soothe

Directions For numbers 6–10, choose the word pair that best completes each analogy. Darken the circle by the word pair you choose.

6. desert : sand :: _____
   Ⓐ ocean : deep
   Ⓑ ocean : blue
   Ⓒ ocean : salty
   Ⓓ ocean : water

7. blueprint : architect :: _____
   Ⓐ x-ray : cure
   Ⓑ x-ray : bones
   Ⓒ x-ray : doctor
   Ⓓ x-ray : technology

8. universe : vast :: _____
   Ⓐ cottage : cute
   Ⓑ cottage : humble
   Ⓒ cottage : small
   Ⓓ cottage : house

9. water : fluid :: _____
   Ⓐ boulder : still
   Ⓑ boulder : hard
   Ⓒ boulder : enormous
   Ⓓ boulder : granite

10. new : fresh :: _____
    Ⓐ old : antique
    Ⓑ old : stale
    Ⓒ old : hard
    Ⓓ old : young

GO ON ⇨

Name _____ Date _____

Multiple Choice Analogies

(Directions) For numbers 11–15, choose the word that best completes each analogy. Darken the circle by the word you choose. Tell why the analogy works or what it is comparing.

11. embark : disembark :: possess : ?   Ⓐ repossess   Ⓑ dispossess   Ⓒ possession

_____

12. 10 : 50 :: 20 : ?   Ⓐ 25   Ⓑ 80   Ⓒ 100

_____

13. bad : worst :: good : ?   Ⓐ better   Ⓑ best   Ⓒ fair

_____

14. 15 : 45 :: 100 : ?   Ⓐ 25   Ⓑ 200   Ⓒ 300

_____

15. soaked : damp :: freezing : ?   Ⓐ frozen   Ⓑ cool   Ⓒ frigid

_____

(Directions) For numbers 16–21, choose the word pair that best completes each analogy. Darken the circle by the word pair you choose.

16. she : hers :: _____
   Ⓐ he : him
   Ⓑ he : he's
   Ⓒ he : his
   Ⓓ he : himself

17. bright : brightness :: _____
   Ⓐ happy : happiest
   Ⓑ happy : joyful
   Ⓒ happy : happier
   Ⓓ happy : happiness

18. twelve : three :: _____
   Ⓐ forty-eight : twelve
   Ⓑ forty-eight : four
   Ⓒ forty-eight : eight
   Ⓓ forty-eight : ninety-six

19. agree : disagree :: _____
   Ⓐ close : shut
   Ⓑ close : disclose
   Ⓒ close : slam
   Ⓓ close : closeness

20. small : miniscule :: _____
   Ⓐ big : tall
   Ⓑ big : large
   Ⓒ big : enormous
   Ⓓ big : bigger

21. patch : dispatch :: _____
   Ⓐ miss : mistake
   Ⓑ miss : dismiss
   Ⓒ miss : remiss
   Ⓓ miss : missive

Supplying Words

Directions To complete these analogies, you will use words that you already know. Read the first word pair, and decide how the two words are related. Then, complete the analogy with a word that will give the second word pair the same relationship. There may be more than one correct answer.

1. picture : illustration :: song : _____

2. man : woman :: boy : _____

3. spider : insect :: _____ : reptile

4. birds : flock :: _____ : colony

5. seed : sprout :: sprout : _____

6. architect : design :: construction worker : _____

7. teacher : profession :: _____ : game

8. ride : bike :: _____ : truck

9. red : color :: _____ : shape

10. breakfast : morning :: supper : _____

11. hockey : sport :: checkers : _____

12. revolve : orbit :: rotate : _____

GO ON ⇨

In Your Own Words

(Directions) **Read each analogy. Think about how the second word pair is related. Then, complete the analogy with a word that gives the first word pair the same relationship. There may be more than one correct answer.**

13. _____ : moon :: solar : sun

14. _____ : liquid :: oxygen : gas

15. snake : _____ :: rodent : prey

16. commence : _____ :: finish : end

17. _____ : lungs :: digestion : stomach

18. basketball : _____ :: soccer : kick

19. dictionary : _____ :: encyclopedia : subjects

20. meter : _____ :: cup : ounces

21. _____ : sun :: moon : Earth

22. _____ : sleep :: bathroom : shower

23. _____ : mammal :: snake : reptile

24. _____ : shutter :: eye : pupil

(Directions) **Read each analogy. Think about how the second word pair is related. Think of a word to go with the second word that relates to it in the same way. Write the word. There may be more than one correct answer.**

25. _____ : brick :: smooth : window

26. _____ : shampoo :: body : soap

27. _____ : quiet :: ceiling : floor

28. _____ : house :: bench : park

29. _____ : ice :: sled : snow

30. _____ : tug :: push : shove

Opposite or Alike?

An analogy can compare antonyms or synonyms.

Look at this example.
forward : backward :: upward : _____

downward   sideward

Think: How do forward and backward relate to each other? Forward is the antonym of backward. Which word is the antonym for upward?

Answer: Downward is the antonym for upward, so **downward** completes this analogy.

Now look at this example.
instructions : directions :: answers : _____

questions   solutions

Think: How do instructions and directions relate to each other? Instructions is a synonym of directions. Which word is a synonym for answers?

Answer: Solutions is the synonym for answers, so **solutions** completes this analogy.

(**Directions**) Read each analogy. Write *antonyms* or *synonyms* to describe the relationship between the first two words. Then, write a word from the box to complete the analogy.

foolish	stutter	bendable	rigid	athletic	robust

1. awkward : graceful :: clumsy : _____

antonyms or synonyms _____

2. brave : courageous :: hearty : _____

antonyms or synonyms _____

3. cringe : recoil :: stammer : _____

antonyms or synonyms _____

4. limber : stiff :: flexible : _____

antonyms or synonyms _____

(GO ON ⇒)

Opposite or Alike?

(**Directions**) Read each analogy. Write *antonyms* or *synonyms* to describe the rela[tion] between the first two words. Then, write a word (or words) from the box to complete the

| soaked | destroy | fanciful | stilted | justify | ancient | happy |
| state-of-the-art | worry | arid | dull | recollect | cast aside | soothe |

5. envision : foresee :: remember : _____

antonyms or synonyms _____

6. damp : moist :: dry : _____

antonyms or synonyms _____

7. harbor : keep safe :: reject : _____

antonyms or synonyms _____

8. diligent : careless :: practical : _____

antonyms or synonyms _____

9. lively : lackluster :: brilliant : _____

antonyms or synonyms _____

10. ponder : consider :: explain : _____

antonyms or synonyms _____

11. stimulate : excite :: relax : _____

antonyms or synonyms _____

12. forge : create :: melt : _____

antonyms or synonyms _____

13. dilapidated : mint :: antique : _____

antonyms or synonyms _____

14. melodious : jarring :: flowing : _____

antonyms or synonyms _____

15. diligent : lazy :: discontented : _____

antonyms or synonyms _____

Analogy-Wiz

Create two antonym analogies and two synonym analogies. Take turns with your classmates, reading the first pair and the third word. Choose one classmate to tell if it is a synonym or an antonym analogy. Ask another classmate to give a possible fourth word to complete the analogy.

A Piece of the Pie

An analogy can compare parts of a whole or a member to its group.

Look at this example.

finger : hand :: toe : _____   toenail   foot

Think: How do finger and hand relate to each other? A finger is a part of a hand. What is a toe a part of?

Answer: A toe is a part of a foot, so **foot** completes this analogy.

Now look at this example.
aspirin : medicine :: raisin : _____   grape   fruit

Think: How do aspirin and medicine relate to each other? An aspirin is a kind of medicine. Of what group is a raisin a part?

Answer: A raisin is a fruit, so **fruit** completes this analogy.

(**Directions**) These analogies compare parts of a whole or members of a group. **Read each analogy. Choose a word from the box that shows the same type of relationship, and write it on the line to complete the analogy.**

gathering	grain	rain	hobby	building	cloud

1. thunderstorm : weather :: cumulus : _____

2. skeleton : body :: frame : _____

3. cotton : fiber :: wheat : _____

4. football : sport :: collecting : _____

(GO ON ⇨)

A Piece of the Pie

(**Directions**) These analogies compare parts of a whole or members of a group. R
analogy. Choose a word from the box that shows the same type of relationship, and wr
to complete the analogy.

teeth	country	Web site	mail	arm	communication	animal
ocean	clothing	toiletry	furniture	cat	government	city

5. Maryland : state :: Baltimore : _____

6. Buddhism : religion :: democracy : _____

7. toaster : appliance :: bureau : _____

8. Doberman : dog :: calico : _____

9. Gobi : desert :: Atlantic : _____

10. shirt : wardrobe :: toothpaste : _____

11. girl : human :: lioness : _____

12. knee : leg :: elbow: _____

13. page : book :: Web page : _____

14. signature : check :: postage : _____

15. painting : art :: writing : _____

Analogy-Wiz

Write the first half of an analogy that compares a part to a whole, or a part to a
group. Trade analogies with a classmate and complete each other's analogies. Talk about your
completed analogies. Do you agree that they work? What makes them work?

What Happens and Why

An analogy can compare causes and effects.

Look at this example.
success : confidence :: failure : _____

contentment   frustration

Think: What is the relationship between success and confidence? Success causes confidence, so confidence is the effect of success. What is the effect of failure?

Answer: Failure can cause frustration, so **frustration** completes this analogy.

Now look at this example.
infection : germs :: health : _____

cleanliness   disease

Think: What is the relationship between infection and germs? Infection is caused by germs, so infection is the effect of germs. What is health caused by, or what is health the effect of?

Answer: Health is the effect of cleanliness, so **cleanliness** completes this analogy.

(Directions) Read each analogy in Column A. Look at the first word pair. Which word is the cause? What is the effect? Choose a word from Column B that shows the same type of relationship, and write its letter on the line to complete the analogy.

Column A	Column B
1. frivolousness : waste :: conservation : _____	**a.** disagreement
2. overwork : exhaustion :: idleness : _____	**b.** awareness
3. accident : carelessness :: safety : _____	**c.** savings
4. harmony : agreement :: discord : _____	**d.** boredom

(GO ON ⇨)

     Analogies 6–8, SV 6908-6

What Happens and Why

Directions Read each analogy in Column A. Look at the first word pair. Which word is the cause? What is the effect? Choose a word from Column B that shows the same type of relationship, and write its letter on the line to complete the analogy.

Column A   **Column B**

5. exploration : discovery :: research : _____   **a.** success

6. discussion : understanding :: argument : _____   **b.** education

7. mistakes : ignorance :: successes : _____   **c.** joy

8. mistrust : dishonesty :: trust : _____   **d.** spite

9. practice : skill :: diligence : _____   **e.** knowledge

10. light : clarity :: darkness : _____   **f.** resentment

11. pain : injury :: comfort : _____   **g.** sweat

12. loss : sorrow :: reunion : _____   **h.** truthfulness

13. cooperate : succeed :: argue : _____   **i.** healing

14. cold : shiver :: heat : _____   **j.** confusion

15. laughter : humor :: sorrow : _____   **k.** impede

Analogy-Wiz

Write a cause-and-effect analogy. Be sure the cause and the effect are in the same place in each word pair of your analogy. If the first word pair compares a cause to an effect, the second pair should, too. If the first word pair compares an effect to its cause, then the second word pair should follow the same order. Share your analogies as a class. Discuss whether each analogy makes sense.

Look and Listen

Some analogies compare homophones, rhymes, or grammar.

Look at these examples and the answer choices for each one.

A. flu : flew :: beet : ?   grew   beat   eat
B. crumb : drum :: follow : ?   wallow   lead   after
C. go : went :: bend : ?   break   bent   bending

Think: What type of analogy is each example? How do the first two words compare? Which answer choice has the same relationship with the third word?

Answers: A. *Flu* and *flew* are homophones. They are words with the same sound but different meanings. *Beet* has the same sound as *beat*, so **beat** completes analogy A.
B. *Crumb* and *drum* are words that rhyme. *Wallow* rhymes with *follow*, so **wallow** completes analogy B.
C. *Went* is the past tense of *go*. *Bent* is the past tense of *bend*, so **bent** completes analogy C.

Directions Read each analogy. Write *homophone*, *rhyme*, or *grammar* on the line. Then, choose a word from the word box to complete each analogy. Write it on the line.

wire	yours	me	delivering	twist	presence	noodle	higher

1. horse : hoarse :: hire : _____

Type of Analogy _____

2. create : creating :: deliver : _____

Type of Analogy _____

3. finger : linger :: poodle : _____

Type of Analogy _____

4. he : his :: you : _____

Type of Analogy _____

5. canister : banister :: wrist : _____

Type of Analogy _____   (GO ON ⇨)

6. drier : dryer :: presents : _____

Type of Analogy _____

Look and Listen

(**Directions**) Read each analogy. Write *homophone*, *rhyme*, or *grammar* on the line. Then, choose a word from the word box to complete each analogy. Write it on the line.

rest	darkness	chord	knight	reassess	surround
busy	businesses	demise	we're	relation	byway

7. originate : hesitate :: highway : _____

Type of Analogy _____

8. they : they're :: we : _____

Type of Analogy _____

9. history : mystery :: surprise : _____

Type of Analogy _____

10. bough : bow :: cord : _____

Type of Analogy _____

11. darker : marker :: around : _____

Type of Analogy _____

12. flour : flower :: night : _____

Type of Analogy _____

13. company : companies :: business : _____

Type of Analogy _____

14. willow : pillow :: blessed : _____

Type of Analogy _____

15. direct : redirect :: assess : _____

Type of Analogy _____

16. dictate : dictation :: relate : _____

Type of Analogy _____

Analogy-Wiz

On separate slips of paper, write one word pair for each type of analogy—homophone, rhyme, and grammar. Put your analogies into a hat or bowl with the ones written by the rest of the class. Form two teams with the class. Take turns completing an analogy pair from the bowl. If the class agrees that an analogy is true, that team gets a point. Then, the second team has a turn. The team with the most points wins.

What's the Use?

Some analogies compare uses of things, who might use them, or what people do.

Look at these examples and the answer choices for each one.

A. awl : split :: vise : ?   mend   grip   part

B. tools : carpenter :: data : ?   information   scientist   architect

C. physician : cure :: instructor : ?   teach   control   entertain

Think: What type of analogy is each example? How do the first two words compare? Which answer choice has the same relationship with the third word?

Answers: A. An awl is a tool that splits. A vice is a tool that grips, so **grip** completes analogy A.

B. Tools are used by a carpenter. Data is used by a scientist, so **scientist** completes analogy B.

C. Cure is what a physician does. Teach is what an instructor does, so **teach** completes analogy C.

(Directions) Read each analogy. Write *use*, *who uses*, or *what people do* on the line. Then, choose a word from the word box to complete each analogy. Write it on the line.

lamp	surgeon	mathematician	meteorologists
historian	illuminate	machinery	air pressure

1. comb : untangle :: bulb : _____

   Type of Analogy _____

2. blueprint : architect :: figures : _____

   Type of Analogy _____

3. clues : detective :: artifacts : _____

   Type of Analogy _____

4. defend : lawyer :: operate : _____

   Type of Analogy _____

5. compass : direction :: barometer : _____

   Type of Analogy _____

GO ON ⇨

What's the Use?

(Directions) Read each analogy. Write *use, who uses,* or *what people do* on the line. Then, choose a word from the word box to complete each analogy. Write it on the line.

fireplace	conductor	comedian	support	writer	runway
pilot	certify	artist	illustrator	musician	contain

6. scythe : mow :: fence : _____

Type of Analogy _____

7. protect : police officer :: entertain : _____

Type of Analogy _____

8. keyboard : typist :: instrument : _____

Type of Analogy _____

9. film : photographer :: canvas : _____

Type of Analogy _____

10. clarify : editor :: describe : _____

Type of Analogy _____

11. label : identify :: license : _____

Type of Analogy _____

12. glasses : magnify :: crutches : _____

Type of Analogy _____

Analogy-Wiz

Read each analogy pair. Choose a pair from the box that compares words in the same way. Write the letter of the pair you choose on the line. Write a sentence explaining what makes each analogy work.

a. animals : biologist	b. water : thirst	c. rollercoaster : entertainment

1. food : dietitian :: _____

_____

_____

2. automobile : transportation :: _____

_____

_____

Name _____   Date _____

What's It Like?

| Analogies often describe things or tell about their characteristics. |

Look at these examples and the answer choices for each one.

A. rabbit : timid :: lion : ?   large   fierce   pride
B. bacteria : miniscule :: whale : ?   ocean   mammal   huge
C. turtle : amphibian :: snake : ?   reptile   venomous   slither

Think: What type of characteristic is being compared in each example? What do the first two words tell you? Which answer choice has the same relationship with the third word?

Answers: A. Timid describes the way a rabbit acts. A lion acts fierce, so **fierce** completes analogy A.

B. Miniscule describes the size of bacteria. The size of a whale is huge, so **huge** completes analogy B.

C. Amphibian tells what animal kingdom a turtle is part of. A snake is part of the reptile kingdom, so **reptile** completes analogy C.

(**Directions**) Read each analogy. In your own words, describe what characteristic is being compared. Then, choose a word from the word box to complete each analogy. Write it on the line.

| paper   entertaining   solid   metal   capable   light   amuse   old |

1. encyclopedia : heavy :: pamphlet : _____

Characteristic _____

2. mystery : intrigue :: comedy : _____

Characteristic _____

3. infant : helpless :: adult : _____

Characteristic _____

4. sponge : porous :: steel : _____

Characteristic _____

5. textbook : informative :: novel : _____   (GO ON ⇨)

Characteristic _____

What's It Like?

(**Directions**) Read each analogy. In your own words, describe what characteristic is being compared. Then, choose a word from the word box to complete each analogy. Write it on the line.

wool	carnivore	uninhabited	tuft	strength	abrasive
narrow	predictable	ocean	strong	clear	flowing

6. ocean : vast :: stream : _____

Characteristic _____

7. weather : changeable :: tides : _____

Characteristic _____

8. elephant : herbivore :: cheetah : _____

Characteristic _____

9. marathon runner : endurance :: weight lifter : _____

Characteristic _____

10. porcelain : fragile :: ceramic : _____

Characteristic _____

11. New York : populous :: wilderness : _____

Characteristic _____

12. glass : smooth :: sandpaper : _____

Characteristic _____

Analogy-Wiz

Read each analogy pair. Choose a pair from the box that compares words in the same way. Write the letter of the pair you choose on the line. Tell why the analogy works.

a. stone : rigid	b. universe : vast	c. water : drop

1. clay : flexible :: _____

_____

2. sand : grain :: _____

_____

Mini-Crosswords

Directions These tiny crossword puzzles each represent an old saying. Complete each analogy using words from the word box. Then, unscramble the words to find the saying. Once you know the saying, fit its words into the mini-crossword. Some of the letters are already in place to help you.

actions	heads	than	louder	are	speak
than	better	one	two	words	

A.

1. listen : hear :: talk : _____

2. mind : thoughts :: body : _____

3. wig : wag :: thin : _____

4. new : newer :: loud : _____

5. paragraph : sentences :: sentence : _____

B.

1. better : best :: good : _____

2. ten : five :: four : _____

3. shoes : feet :: hats : _____

4. did : do :: were : _____

5. addition : zero :: multiplication : _____

6. beg : bag :: then : _____

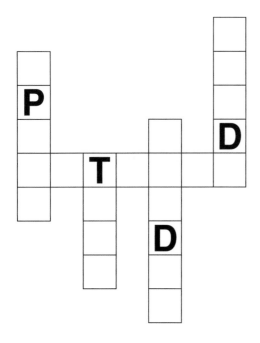

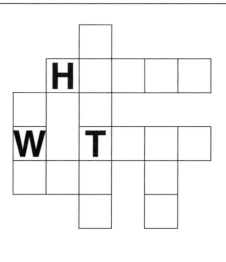

Getting There

The analogies in this exercise are all related in some way to travel and transportation.

Look at this example.
family : car :: tour group :
Ⓐ train   Ⓑ airplane   Ⓒ bus   Ⓓ bicycle

Think: How does the first word pair relate? A family travels in a car. How does a tour group usually travel?

Answer: A tour group would most likely be on a bus, so **bus** completes this analogy. Darken the circle by bus.

Directions Read each analogy. Decide how the first word pair is related. Choose the word that relates to the third word in the same way. Darken the circle by your choice.

1. automobile : accelerator :: bicycle :
   Ⓐ feet   Ⓑ person   Ⓒ pedals   Ⓓ slow

2. jet : air :: barge :
   Ⓐ water   Ⓑ garbage   Ⓒ large   Ⓓ transport

3. balloon : hot air :: speedboat :
   Ⓐ lake   Ⓑ gasoline   Ⓒ summer   Ⓓ wind

4. canoe : paddle :: sailboat :
   Ⓐ float   Ⓑ ocean   Ⓒ wind   Ⓓ motor

5. cruise ship : entertainment :: company car :
   Ⓐ road   Ⓑ travel   Ⓒ vehicle   Ⓓ business

GO ON ⇨

Getting There

Directions Read each analogy. Decide how the first word pair is related. Choose the word that relates to the third word in the same way. Darken the circle by your choice.

6. walk : leisurely :: jet :
    Ⓐ swiftly   Ⓑ air   © cross-country   Ⓓ passengers

7. drive : active :: ride :
    Ⓐ car   Ⓑ passive   © relax   Ⓓ observe

8. subway : below :: air traffic :
    Ⓐ airplanes   Ⓑ airport   © control   Ⓓ above

9. tricycle : toddler :: mountain bike :
    Ⓐ pilot   Ⓑ teen   © two   Ⓓ rough

10. surfboard : ocean :: snowmobile :
    Ⓐ northern   Ⓑ noisy   © snow   Ⓓ cold

11. dinghy : private :: tour boat :
    Ⓐ public   Ⓑ scenic   © tourism   Ⓓ vacation

12. motorcycle : exposed :: automobile :
    Ⓐ safety   Ⓑ enclosed   © highway   Ⓓ group

13. car : steering wheel :: hot-air balloon :
    Ⓐ flame   Ⓑ rudder   © wind direction   Ⓓ pilot

14. airplane : pilot :: vessel :
    Ⓐ ship   Ⓑ ocean   © captain   Ⓓ crew

15. automobile : traffic signal :: airplane :
    Ⓐ control panel   Ⓑ co-pilot   © flight path   Ⓓ air traffic control

Analogy-Wiz

Write your own travel/transportation analogy with four answer choices. Trade analogies with a classmate to complete. Discuss your analogies and the answers. Do you agree that the analogies make sense? Why or why not?

Get Up and Go

The analogies in this exercise are all related in some way to sports.

Look at this example.

baseball : inning :: basketball :

- Ⓐ period
- Ⓑ half
- Ⓒ quarter
- Ⓓ point

Think: How does the first word pair relate? Baseball is played in innings. What are the parts of a basketball game called?

Answer: A basketball game is divided into quarters, so **quarter** completes this analogy. Darken the circle by quarter.

(**Directions**) **Read each analogy. Decide how the first word pair is related. Choose the word that relates to the third word in the same way. Darken the circle by your choice.**

1. goal : hockey :: run :
- Ⓐ race
- Ⓑ baseball
- Ⓒ home
- Ⓓ score

2. golf ball : club :: hockey puck :
- Ⓐ stick
- Ⓑ flat
- Ⓒ goal
- Ⓓ ice

3. football : field :: basketball :
- Ⓐ arena
- Ⓑ basket
- Ⓒ court
- Ⓓ gymnasium

4. baseball : bat :: tennis :
- Ⓐ court
- Ⓑ match
- Ⓒ net
- Ⓓ racket

(GO ON ⇨)

Get Up and Go

Directions Read each analogy. Decide how the first word pair is related. Choose the word that relates to the third word in the same way. Darken the circle by your choice.

5. distance : marathon runner :: strength :
   - Ⓐ weight lifter
   - Ⓑ muscle
   - Ⓒ stride
   - Ⓓ exercise

6. car race : speed :: archery :
   - Ⓐ arrow
   - Ⓑ target
   - Ⓒ accuracy
   - Ⓓ bull's-eye

7. pool : swimmer :: track :
   - Ⓐ runner
   - Ⓑ oval
   - Ⓒ starting line
   - Ⓓ lane

8. stick : lacrosse :: mitt :
   - Ⓐ goalie
   - Ⓑ catch
   - Ⓒ baseball
   - Ⓓ pitch

9. boxing : ring :: wrestling :
   - Ⓐ strength
   - Ⓑ three count
   - Ⓒ spectators
   - Ⓓ mat

10. surfboard : wave :: skateboard :
    - Ⓐ wheels
    - Ⓑ wax
    - Ⓒ pads
    - Ⓓ dry

11. rollerskate : wheel :: ice skate :
    - Ⓐ ice
    - Ⓑ blade
    - Ⓒ winter
    - Ⓓ figure

12. sprinter : speed :: gymnast :
    - Ⓐ size
    - Ⓑ agility
    - Ⓒ height
    - Ⓓ chalk

13. ski poles : skier :: trekking poles :
    - Ⓐ balance
    - Ⓑ support
    - Ⓒ hiker
    - Ⓓ lightweight

14. safety harness : climber :: helmet :
    - Ⓐ circus clown
    - Ⓑ entertainer
    - Ⓒ football player
    - Ⓓ barrel racer

Analogy-Wiz

Write your own sports analogy. Take turns reading your analogies in class, leaving off the last word. Call on volunteers for the answer. Remember, there might be more than one right answer to some analogies.

There's an Art to It

The analogies in this exercise are all related in some way to the arts.

Look at this example.
flower arrangement : still life :: person :
Ⓐ live   Ⓑ pose   Ⓒ active   Ⓓ portrait

Think: How does the first word pair relate? When an artist paints a flower arrangement, it is called a still life. What is it called when an artist paints a person?

Answer: When an artist paints a person, it is called a portrait, so **portrait** completes this analogy. Darken the circle by portrait.

(Directions) Read each analogy. Decide how the first word pair is related. Choose the word that relates to the third word in the same way. Darken the circle by your choice.

1. pencil : sketch :: stone :
Ⓐ chisel   Ⓑ sculpture   Ⓒ rock   Ⓓ marble

2. creative : imaginative :: bright :
Ⓐ shadow   Ⓑ deep   Ⓒ vivid   Ⓓ dim

3. painter : canvas :: photographer :
Ⓐ film   Ⓑ camera   Ⓒ pictures   Ⓓ capture

4. paint : brush :: sculpt :
Ⓐ clay   Ⓑ chisel   Ⓒ statue   Ⓓ create

5. gallery : sell :: museum :
Ⓐ old   Ⓑ artists   Ⓒ collections   Ⓓ display

(GO ON ⇨)

There's an Art to It

Directions Read each analogy. Decide how the first word pair is related. Choose the word that relates to the third word in the same way. Darken the circle by your choice.

6. potter's wheel : clay :: palette :
   - A color
   - B paint
   - C artist
   - D brush

7. symmetry : balance :: asymmetry :
   - A inconsistency
   - B sameness
   - C equality
   - D parallel

8. model : portrait :: nature :
   - A natural
   - B wildlife
   - C landscape
   - D painting

9. etching : remove :: collage :
   - A add
   - B paste
   - C objects
   - D variety

10. vague : detailed :: traditional :
    - A ancient
    - B complicated
    - C spectacular
    - D contemporary

11. picture : frame :: sculpture :
    - A display
    - B hang
    - C pedestal
    - D mold

12. clay : pottery :: paper :
    - A origami
    - B wrinkle
    - C fragile
    - D temporary

13. library : librarian :: museum :
    - A visitors
    - B benefactor
    - C curator
    - D building

14. photographs : photography :: buildings :
    - A contractor
    - B architecture
    - C urban
    - D skyscrapers

15. brush : painting :: pen :
    - A fine
    - B hand
    - C calligraphy
    - D pencil

Analogy-Wiz

Make a picture analogy about art. First, think of an art analogy. Then, find pictures to represent each word. Attach the pictures to a piece of cardboard or construction paper. Write the words beneath the pictures. Display your picture analogies in your classroom.

Figure It Out

The analogies in this exercise are all related in some way to mathematics.

Look at this example.

words : language :: numbers :

Ⓐ operation

Ⓑ product

Ⓒ math

Ⓓ figures

 Think: How does the first word pair relate? Words make up language. Which answer describes what numbers make up?

Answer: Numbers make up math, so **math** completes this analogy. Darken the circle by math.

(Directions) Read each analogy. Decide how the first word pair is related. Choose the word that relates to the third word in the same way. Darken the circle by your choice.

1. addition : subtraction :: multiplication :
Ⓐ minus
Ⓑ division
Ⓒ multiply
Ⓓ numbers

2. area : within :: perimeter :
Ⓐ distance
Ⓑ feet
Ⓒ around
Ⓓ fence

3. twelve : thirty-six :: twenty-one :
Ⓐ seven
Ⓑ eighty-four
Ⓒ sixty-three
Ⓓ eleven

4. twelve : factorable :: eleven :
Ⓐ prime
Ⓑ ten
Ⓒ divisible
Ⓓ odd

5. quart : cup :: gallon :
Ⓐ pint
Ⓑ half-gallon
Ⓒ quart
Ⓓ liquid

6. chronometer : time :: odometer :
Ⓐ temperature
Ⓑ speed
Ⓒ width
Ⓓ distance

(GO ON ⇨)

Figure It Out

Directions Read each analogy. Decide how the first word pair is related. Choose the word that relates to the third word in the same way. Darken the circle by your choice.

7. triangle : three :: octagon :
- Ⓐ eight
- Ⓑ six
- Ⓒ figure
- Ⓓ five

8. addition : sum :: subtraction :
- Ⓐ less
- Ⓑ minus
- Ⓒ difference
- Ⓓ remove

9. mile : distance :: cubic inch :
- Ⓐ fill
- Ⓑ area
- Ⓒ height
- Ⓓ volume

10. 90° : perpendicular :: 180° :
- Ⓐ circle
- Ⓑ straight
- Ⓒ angle
- Ⓓ degrees

11. round : oval :: square :
- Ⓐ triangle
- Ⓑ four
- Ⓒ cube
- Ⓓ rectangle

12. one : one half :: one hundred :
- Ⓐ two hundred
- Ⓑ fifty
- Ⓒ twenty-five
- Ⓓ one fourth

13. yard : length :: kilogram :
- Ⓐ volume
- Ⓑ mass
- Ⓒ distance
- Ⓓ gram

14. height : feet :: depth :
- Ⓐ cubic feet
- Ⓑ degrees
- Ⓒ fathoms
- Ⓓ gallons

15. multiplication : product :: division :
- Ⓐ quotient
- Ⓑ difference
- Ⓒ dividend
- Ⓓ divisor

Analogy-Wiz

Exercises 3 and 12 are examples of number analogies. Write the first word pair for three of your own number analogies. Trade your analogies with a classmate and complete each other's analogies. (There may be an infinite number of ways to complete some of them!) Share your completed analogies. Discuss whether they are true number analogies.

Where in the World

The analogies in this exercise are all related in some way to geography.

Look at this example.

mountain : height :: ocean :

Ⓐ depth   Ⓑ liquid   Ⓒ Pacific   Ⓓ volume

Think: How does the first word pair relate? Mountains are usually measured by their height. Which answer describes the way we measure oceans?

Answer: Oceans are usually measured by their depth, so **depth** completes this analogy. Darken the circle by depth.

(Directions) Read each analogy. Decide how the first word pair is related. Choose the word that relates to the third word in the same way. Darken the circle by your choice.

1. latitude : north :: longitude :

Ⓐ height   Ⓑ south   Ⓒ east   Ⓓ equator

2. tropical : rain forest :: arid :

Ⓐ desert   Ⓑ humidity   Ⓒ equator   Ⓓ dry

3. Atlantic : ocean :: Katahdin :

Ⓐ Maine   Ⓑ mountain   Ⓒ north   Ⓓ United States

4. Austin : Texas :: Sacramento :

Ⓐ capital   Ⓑ state   Ⓒ California   Ⓓ western

5. China : Asia :: Brazil :

Ⓐ country   Ⓑ South America   Ⓒ temperate   Ⓓ Antarctica

Name _____ Date _____

Where in the World

(**Directions**) Read each analogy. Decide how the first word pair is related. Choose the word that relates to the third word in the same way. Darken the circle by your choice.

6. Mississippi River : United States :: Nile River :
   Ⓐ Asia   Ⓑ South America   Ⓒ Australia   Ⓓ Egypt

7. desert : dune :: ocean :
   Ⓐ water   Ⓑ salt   Ⓒ wave   Ⓓ shore

8. latitude : longitude :: vertical :
   Ⓐ horizontal   Ⓑ north   Ⓒ location   Ⓓ poles

9. equator : sweltering :: pole :
   Ⓐ axis   Ⓑ north   Ⓒ frigid   Ⓓ south

10. pyramids : Egypt :: Amazon :
    Ⓐ South America   Ⓑ river   Ⓒ tropical   Ⓓ Asia

11. shoreline : ocean :: tree line :
    Ⓐ forest   Ⓑ range   Ⓒ mountain   Ⓓ altitude

12. Red : sea :: Indian :
    Ⓐ mountain range   Ⓑ continent   Ⓒ country   Ⓓ ocean

13. Oregon : Pacific :: Maine :
    Ⓐ Atlantic   Ⓑ west   Ⓒ state   Ⓓ east

14. Washington, D.C. : United States :: Madrid :
    Ⓐ France   Ⓑ Spain   Ⓒ Germany   Ⓓ Italy

15. northern hemisphere : Canada :: southern hemisphere :
    Ⓐ United States   Ⓑ Greenland   Ⓒ India   Ⓓ Australia

Analogy-Wiz

Use reference materials or the Internet to write an analogy that relates to geography. Find pictures for the words you choose. Display your analogy and pictures in your classroom.

It Was a Dark and Stormy Night...

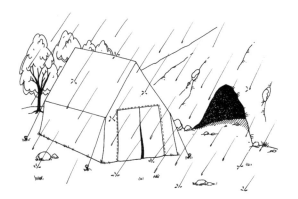

The analogies in this exercise are all related in some way to weather.

Look at this example.

sun : ray :: rain :

Ⓐ wet

Ⓑ drop

Ⓒ fall

Ⓓ storm

Think: How does the first word pair relate? The sun reaches the Earth in rays. Which answer describes the way rain reaches the Earth?

Answer: Rain reaches the Earth in drops, so **drop** completes this analogy. Darken the circle by drop.

(**Directions**) Read each analogy. Decide how the first word pair is related. Choose the word that relates to the third word in the same way. Darken the circle by your choice.

1. ocean : tsunami :: mountain :

Ⓐ volcano

Ⓑ Mt. Vesuvius

Ⓒ altitude

Ⓓ hurricane

2. lava : volcano :: funnel cloud :

Ⓐ baking

Ⓑ rainstorm

Ⓒ tornado

Ⓓ disaster

3. biologist : life :: meteorologist :

Ⓐ rain forest

Ⓑ weather

Ⓒ meteors

Ⓓ space

4. water : island :: atmosphere :

Ⓐ air

Ⓑ breathe

Ⓒ oxygen

Ⓓ Earth

(GO ON ⇨)

Name _____ Date _____

It Was a Dark and Stormy Night...

Directions Read each analogy. Decide how the first word pair is related. Choose the word that relates to the third word in the same way. Darken the circle by your choice.

5. cloud : sky :: fog :
- Ⓐ mist
- Ⓑ low
- Ⓒ ground
- Ⓓ unclear

6. hot : heat stroke :: cold :
- Ⓐ snow
- Ⓑ winter
- Ⓒ wind
- Ⓓ hypothermia

7. thermometer : temperature :: barometer :
- Ⓐ atmospheric pressure
- Ⓑ wind chill
- Ⓒ cloud cover
- Ⓓ stability

8. wind speed : tornado :: Richter scale :
- Ⓐ volcano
- Ⓑ earthquake
- Ⓒ hurricane
- Ⓓ tsunami

9. blue sky : clear :: gray sky :
- Ⓐ color
- Ⓑ gusty
- Ⓒ overcast
- Ⓓ sunshine

10. thunder : sound :: lightning :
- Ⓐ danger
- Ⓑ chain
- Ⓒ rain
- Ⓓ appearance

11. poles : frozen :: equator :
- Ⓐ humid
- Ⓑ invisible
- Ⓒ center
- Ⓓ Africa

12. spring : rain :: winter :
- Ⓐ cold
- Ⓑ frostbite
- Ⓒ snow
- Ⓓ ice

13. atlas : travel :: weather map :
- Ⓐ meteorologist
- Ⓑ forecast
- Ⓒ directions
- Ⓓ newscast

14. snow : blizzard :: rain :
- Ⓐ sprinkle
- Ⓑ monsoon
- Ⓒ cumulus cloud
- Ⓓ drizzle

Analogy-Wiz

Draw a line from a word pair in the first column to one in the second column that has the same type of relationship.

hailstorm : hail ::	umbrella : rain
rain : drop ::	flurry : blizzard
parka : snow ::	snow : flake
sprinkle : deluge ::	windstorm : sand

Name _____   Date _____

Analogy Scramble

(Directions) Read each analogy. Unscramble the answer choices. Write the correct answer on the lines, beginning with the first line. (There may be more lines than you need.) Then, assemble the letters in the boxes to make the new word that will complete the bonus analogy.

1. blizzard : flurry :: downpour : ?   fgo   zzldire

   ___ ___ ___ ___ ___ ___ ___ ___ ___ ___

2. white : snow :: multihued : ?   waribno   rtwae

   ___ ___ ___ ___ ___ ___ ___ ___ ___ ___

3. she : her :: they : ?   mthe   erhte

   ___ ___ ___ ___ ___ ___ ___ ___ ___ ___

4. numbers : algebra :: shapes : ?   droun   tryomege

   ___ ___ ___ ___ ___ ___ ___ ___ ___ ___

5. jog : race :: practice : ?   ttiioonepcm   pimvroe

   ___ ___ ___ ___ ___ ___ ___ ___ ___ ___

6. railroad : track :: traffic : ?   biletomoau   wighhay

   ___ ___ ___ ___ ___ ___ ___ ___ ___ ___

7. multiply: increase :: divide : ?   eecrasde   sptareae

   ___ ___ ___ ___ ___ ___ ___ ___ ___ ___

8. we : our :: you : ?   ruyo   yuros

   ___ ___ ___ ___ ___ ___ ___ ___ ___ ___

9. height : altitude :: speed : ?   cityolve   tighl

   ___ ___ ___ ___ ___ ___ ___ ___ ___ ___

10. four : eight :: eight : ?   velene   texines

   ___ ___ ___ ___ ___ ___ ___ ___ ___ ___

Bonus Analogy

pieces : puzzle :: words : ?   ___ ___ ___ ___ ___ ___ ___ ___ ___

Wash and Wear

To complete these analogies, you will need to match word pairs that have similar relationships. The analogies in this exercise are all related in some way to materials or clothing.

Look at this example.

gloves : hands ::

Ⓐ vest : shirt   Ⓑ scarf : neck   Ⓒ ring : finger

Think: How does the first word pair relate? Gloves keep our hands warm. Which word pair describes something that keeps another body part warm?

Answer: A scarf keeps our neck warm, so **scarf : neck** completes this analogy. Darken the circle by scarf : neck. Both word pairs describe where warm clothing is worn.

Directions Read each analogy. Decide how the first word pair is related. Choose the word pair that shows the most similar relationship. Darken the circle by your choice. On the line below each analogy, describe the relationship.

1. belt : waist ::

        Ⓐ shoe : sock   Ⓑ shirt : neck   Ⓒ suspenders : shoulders

_____

2. cold : parka ::

        Ⓐ hot : shorts   Ⓑ summer : beach   Ⓒ sunshine : bathing suit

_____

3. collar : neck ::

        Ⓐ lining : coat   Ⓑ cuff : wrist   Ⓒ sock : shoe

_____

(GO ON ⇨)

Wash and Wear

(**Directions**) Read each analogy. Decide how the first word pair is related. Choose the word pair that shows the most similar relationship. Darken the circle by your choice. On the line below each analogy, describe the relationship.

4. cotton : natural ::

      Ⓐ wool : sheep   Ⓑ nylon : fiber   Ⓒ polyester : manmade

_____

5. tuxedo : formal ::

      Ⓐ blue jeans : casual   Ⓑ blue jeans : comfortable   Ⓒ blue jeans : sneakers

_____

6. silk : caress ::

      Ⓐ wool : warm   Ⓑ burlap : chafe   Ⓒ skin : smooth

_____

7. beret : hat ::

      Ⓐ windbreaker : coat   Ⓑ cap : head   Ⓒ head : covering

_____

8. slippers : relaxation ::

      Ⓐ robe : pajamas   Ⓑ athletic shoes : exercise   Ⓒ evening : pajamas

_____

9. wool : sheep ::

      Ⓐ cow : dairy   Ⓑ nylon : stockings   Ⓒ cotton : plant

_____

10. black : tuxedo ::

      Ⓐ green : vibrant   Ⓑ white : bridal gown   Ⓒ blazer : coat

_____

Analogy-Wiz

Make up your own analogy about fashions or fabrics. Find pictures or samples of fabric or fiber for the words you chose. Display your analogy and pictures or samples in a creative way.

It's a Science

To complete these analogies, you will need to match word pairs that have similar relationships. The analogies in this exercise are all related in some way to science.

Look at this example.

oxygen : gas ::
Ⓐ solid : hard
Ⓑ atmosphere : nitrogen
Ⓒ water : liquid

Think: How does the first word pair relate? Oxygen has the properties of a gas. Which word pair describes another thing and its properties?

Answer: Water has the properties of a liquid, so **water : liquid** completes this analogy. Darken the circle by water : liquid.

(Directions) Read each analogy. Decide how the first word pair is related. Choose the word pair that shows the most similar relationship. Darken the circle by your choice.

1. iron : metal ::
Ⓐ coal : mine
Ⓑ diamond : gemstone
Ⓒ Ca : calcium

2. melt : liquid ::
Ⓐ freeze : cold
Ⓑ freeze : ice
Ⓒ freeze : solid

3. attraction : repulsion ::
Ⓐ mirror : reflection
Ⓑ action : reaction
Ⓒ mixture : solution

4. gas : matter ::
Ⓐ gravity : force
Ⓑ laser : sight
Ⓒ electricity : meter

5. magnet : attract ::
Ⓐ north : pole
Ⓑ metal : magnetic
Ⓒ like poles : repel

6. decibel : sound ::
Ⓐ degree : temperature
Ⓑ wave : light
Ⓒ rain : precipitation

7. lever : push ::
Ⓐ pulley : rope
Ⓑ pulley : pull
Ⓒ fulcrum : center

8. mass : weight ::
Ⓐ newton : force
Ⓑ newton : apple
Ⓒ evaporation : condensation

(GO ON ⇨)

It's a Science

(Directions) Read each analogy. Decide how the first word pair is related. Choose the word pair that shows the most similar relationship. Darken the circle by your choice.

9. evaporation : dry ::
- Ⓐ coal : mine
- Ⓑ diamond : precious stone
- Ⓒ condensation : moist

10. all colors : white ::
- Ⓐ spectrum : color
- Ⓑ no color : black
- Ⓒ prism : light

11. blue : cool ::
- Ⓐ red : hot
- Ⓑ white : cold
- Ⓒ yellow : flame

12. heat : expansion ::
- Ⓐ expand : crack
- Ⓑ cold : contraction
- Ⓒ contract : expand

13. centrifugal force : outward ::
- Ⓐ spin : disorient
- Ⓑ push : pull
- Ⓒ gravity : inward

14. Celsius : zero ::
- Ⓐ Fahrenheit : thirty-two
- Ⓑ ice : freezing
- Ⓒ temperature : thermometer

15. buoyancy : float ::
- Ⓐ light : cork
- Ⓑ density : sink
- Ⓒ water : liquid

16. proton : positive ::
- Ⓐ nucleus : center
- Ⓑ electron : negative
- Ⓒ atom : molecule

Analogy-Wiz

With a classmate, create a physical science analogy that you can demonstrate. Before you begin, write a brief paragraph telling how you plan to demonstrate your analogy for your teacher's approval. Share your demonstration with your class.

_____

_____

_____

_____

_____

_____

_____

_____

Stretch Your Vocabulary

To complete these analogies, you will need to match word pairs that have similar relationships. The analogies in this exercise are all related to language.

Look at this example.

create : recreate ::
- Ⓐ enact : reenact
- Ⓑ build : destroy
- Ⓒ fix : fixate
- Ⓓ fun : recreation

Think: How does the first word pair relate? *Create* is the root word of *recreate*, with the prefix *re* added. Which word pair shows the same relationship?

Answer: *Enact* is the root word of *reenact*, with the prefix *re* added, so **enact : reenact** completes this analogy. Darken the circle by enact : reenact.

(Directions) Read each analogy. Decide how the first word pair is related. Choose the word pair that shows the most similar relationship. Darken the circle by your choice.

1. follow : follower ::
   - Ⓐ borrow : borrowing
   - Ⓑ leader : director
   - Ⓒ game : player
   - Ⓓ design : designer

2. remark : remarkable ::
   - Ⓐ say : saying
   - Ⓑ treat : treatable
   - Ⓒ pack : package
   - Ⓓ speak : speaker

3. lonely : loneliest ::
   - Ⓐ far : farthest
   - Ⓑ forlorn : forlornly
   - Ⓒ alone : lonely
   - Ⓓ alone : solitary

4. satisfy : satisfaction ::
   - Ⓐ please : pleased
   - Ⓑ replace : placement
   - Ⓒ clarify : clarification
   - Ⓓ officer : office

5. dishearten : disappoint ::
   - Ⓐ sad : sadden
   - Ⓑ amuse : entertain
   - Ⓒ excitement : excite
   - Ⓓ understanding : confusion

6. distracted : attentive ::
   - Ⓐ satisfied : content
   - Ⓑ quiet : withdrawn
   - Ⓒ unknown : mysterious
   - Ⓓ exciting : dull

(GO ON ⇨)

Stretch Your Vocabulary

Directions Read each analogy. Decide how the first word pair is related. Choose the word pair that shows the most similar relationship. Darken the circle by your choice.

7. defend : defendant ::
- Ⓐ replace : replacement
- Ⓑ discussion : conversation
- Ⓒ embroidery : stitchery
- Ⓓ lawyer : prosecutor

8. reach : attain ::
- Ⓐ choose : choice
- Ⓑ trust : betray
- Ⓒ hope : hopeful
- Ⓓ error : mistake

9. install : installment ::
- Ⓐ guess : guest
- Ⓑ include : count
- Ⓒ postpone : postponement
- Ⓓ wonder : wondrous

10. awe : awesome ::
- Ⓐ unbelievable : incredible
- Ⓑ fear : fearsome
- Ⓒ huge : enormous
- Ⓓ great : greatness

11. calamity : calamitous ::
- Ⓐ event : function
- Ⓑ process : procession
- Ⓒ furnish : furnishings
- Ⓓ disaster : disastrous

12. legend : legendary ::
- Ⓐ travel : traveler
- Ⓑ caution : cautionary
- Ⓒ science : scientist
- Ⓓ parallel : parallelism

13. embarrass : humiliate ::
- Ⓐ sincere : earnest
- Ⓑ show : showmanship
- Ⓒ prank : prankster
- Ⓓ amuse : irritate

14. bestow : deprive ::
- Ⓐ illustrate : show
- Ⓑ describe : explain
- Ⓒ ingenious : ridiculous
- Ⓓ direct : instruct

Analogy-Wiz

Write five language analogies. Tell why the analogies work.

1. _____

2. _____

3. _____

4. _____

5. _____

How Would You Describe It?

To complete these analogies, you will need to match word pairs that have similar relationships. The analogies in this exercise are all related to the characteristics of things.

Look at this example.

school : education ::
- Ⓐ museum : artwork
- Ⓑ water park : entertainment
- Ⓒ monument : Washington
- Ⓓ mall : stores

 Think: How does the first word pair relate? Education describes the purpose of school. Which word pair shows the same relationship?

Answer: Entertainment is the purpose of a water park, so **water park : entertainment** completes this analogy. Darken the circle by water park : entertainment.

(Directions) Read each analogy. Decide how the first word pair is related. What type of characteristic is being compared? Choose the word pair that shows the most similar relationship. Darken the circle by your choice.

1. city : offices ::
- Ⓐ neighborhood : houses
- Ⓑ military : base
- Ⓒ skyscraper : height
- Ⓓ family : home

2. highway : public ::
- Ⓐ lights : traffic
- Ⓑ driveway : private
- Ⓒ sidewalk : pedestrians
- Ⓓ lane : narrow

3. Earth : spherical ::
- Ⓐ ball : bounce
- Ⓑ moon : orbit
- Ⓒ orbit : elliptical
- Ⓓ axis : rotate

4. core : molten ::
- Ⓐ poles : frozen
- Ⓑ crust : outside
- Ⓒ plates : movement
- Ⓓ lava : volcano

5. snake : reptilian ::
- Ⓐ frog : swimmer
- Ⓑ frog : amphibious
- Ⓒ elephant : warm-blooded
- Ⓓ dog : wolf

6. rainbow : multicolored ::
- Ⓐ view : panoramic
- Ⓑ flowers : vibrant
- Ⓒ water : colorless
- Ⓓ colors : primary

(GO ON ⇨)

How Would You Describe It?

Directions Read each analogy. Decide how the first word pair is related. What type of characteristic is being compared? Choose the word pair that shows the most similar relationship. Darken the circle by your choice.

7. song : melodious ::
- Ⓐ howl : wolf
- Ⓑ baby : cry
- Ⓒ sound : decibels
- Ⓓ jackhammer : jarring

8. water : refreshing ::
- Ⓐ food : nourishing
- Ⓑ carrot : vegetable
- Ⓒ rain : moisture
- Ⓓ supper : evening

9. chore : tedious ::
- Ⓐ trash : recycling
- Ⓑ game : checkers
- Ⓒ game : amusing
- Ⓓ dishes : washing

10. cave : dank ::
- Ⓐ forest : dense
- Ⓑ mountain : immense
- Ⓒ ocean : vast
- Ⓓ breeze : refreshing

11. still water : murky ::
- Ⓐ ocean : tides
- Ⓑ mountain stream : clear
- Ⓒ pond : frog
- Ⓓ river : current

12. computer technology : state-of-the-art ::
- Ⓐ keyboard : type
- Ⓑ Internet : world-wide
- Ⓒ typewriter : old-fashioned
- Ⓓ email : instantaneous

13. mountain : awe-inspiring ::
- Ⓐ hill : unremarkable
- Ⓑ mesa : plateau
- Ⓒ butte : plains
- Ⓓ rise : incline

14. mystery : intriguing ::
- Ⓐ comedy : slapstick
- Ⓑ Civil War : history
- Ⓒ horror : frightening
- Ⓓ aliens : science fiction

Analogy-Wiz

From words that you already know, supply the last word for each of these analogies. Decide how the first word pair is related. Think of a word that relates to the third word in the same way. Write it on the line.

lace : fine :: burlap : _____

porcelain : fragile :: steel : _____

rule : imperative :: suggestion : _____

cloudy : overcast :: sunny : _____

Name _____ Date _____

All in a Day's Work

To complete these analogies, you will need to match word pairs
that have similar relationships. The analogies in this exercise are
all related to professions or careers.

Look at this example.

chef : restaurant ::

Ⓐ florist : flowers   Ⓑ scientist : laboratory   Ⓒ engineer : construction

Think: How does the first word pair relate? A restaurant is where a chef works. Which
word pair shows the same relationship?

Answer: A laboratory is one place that a scientist works, so **scientist : laboratory** completes
this analogy. Darken the circle by scientist : laboratory.

(**Directions**) Read each analogy. Decide how the first word pair is related. Choose the word pair
that shows the most similar relationship. Darken the circle by your choice. Then, write a brief
explanation of what the relationship is.

1. police officer : arrest ::

Ⓐ jury : court   Ⓑ lawyer : brief   Ⓒ judge : sentence

_____

2. galaxy : astronomer ::

Ⓐ ocean : sailor   Ⓑ earth : geologist   Ⓒ bread : bakery

_____

3. novel : author ::

Ⓐ building : architect   Ⓑ research : reporter   Ⓒ bricks : mason

_____

(GO ON ⇨)

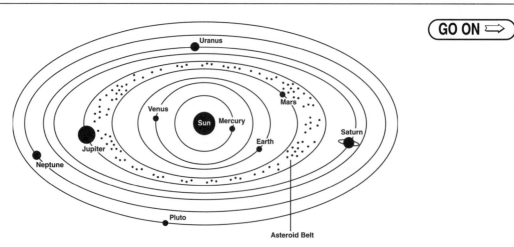

All in a Day's Work

Directions Read each analogy. Decide how the first word pair is related. Choose the word pair that shows the most similar relationship. Darken the circle by your choice. Then, write a brief explanation of what the relationship is.

4. professor : students ::
Ⓐ captain : ship   Ⓑ coach : football   Ⓒ tour guide : tourists

_____

5. patients : physician ::
Ⓐ dental hygiene : dentist   Ⓑ hospital : surgery   Ⓒ animals : veterinarian

_____

6. psychiatrist : discussion ::
Ⓐ athlete : action   Ⓑ astronaut : liftoff   Ⓒ fisher : boat

_____

7. presentation : chef ::
Ⓐ plants : landscaper   Ⓑ finish work : cabinetmaker Ⓒ customers : restaurant

_____

8. patience : childcare worker ::
Ⓐ creativity : artist   Ⓑ crew : captain   Ⓒ votes : politician

_____

9. dictionary : editor ::
Ⓐ programs : computer technician Ⓑ wires : electrician   Ⓒ Internet : librarian

_____

10. voters : politician ::
Ⓐ fire : firefighter   Ⓑ readers : author   Ⓒ film : photographer

_____

Analogy-Wiz

From words that you already know, supply the last word for each of these analogies. Decide how the first word pair is related. Think of a word that relates to the third word in the same way. Write it on the line.

canvas : artist :: paper : _____

surgeon : scalpel :: tailor : _____

beach : lifeguard :: classroom : _____

humor : comedian :: music : _____

An Apple a Day

To complete these analogies, you will need to match word pairs
that have similar relationships. The analogies in this exercise are
all related to health.

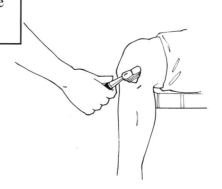

Look at this example.
hammer : reflex ::
Ⓐ needle : stick
Ⓑ blood pressure : cuff
Ⓒ thermometer : temperature
Ⓓ doctor : prescription

Think: How does the first word pair relate? A hammer is used to test a reflex.
Which word pair shows the same relationship?

Answer: A thermometer is used to take a temperature, so **thermometer : temperature**
completes this analogy. Darken the circle by thermometer : temperature.

(Directions) Read each analogy. Decide how the first word pair is related. Choose the word pair
that shows the most similar relationship. Darken the circle by your choice.

1. bandage : cut ::
  Ⓐ bacteria : dirt
  Ⓑ adhesive : bandage
  Ⓒ clean : disinfect
  Ⓓ stitches : incision

2. food : nutrition ::
  Ⓐ cereals : grain
  Ⓑ vegetables : healthy
  Ⓒ water : hydration
  Ⓓ milk : dairy

3. physician : body ::
  Ⓐ dentist : teeth
  Ⓑ doctor : examination
  Ⓒ prescription : medicine
  Ⓓ strength : muscle

4. calcium : bones ::
  Ⓐ oxygen : lungs
  Ⓑ sun : vitamin D
  Ⓒ milk : calcium
  Ⓓ bones : posture

5. stretching : flexibility ::
  Ⓐ sleep : health
  Ⓑ exercise : strength
  Ⓒ vitamins : nutrition
  Ⓓ vitamins : minerals

6. white blood cells : disease ::
  Ⓐ sickness : medicine
  Ⓑ medicine : prevention
  Ⓒ antiseptic : bacteria
  Ⓓ disease : prognosis

GO ON ⇨

Name _____ Date _____

An Apple a Day

(**Directions**) **Read each analogy. Decide how the first word pair is related. Choose the word pair that shows the most similar relationship. Darken the circle by your choice.**

7. bread : grain ::
- Ⓐ fruits : vegetables
- Ⓑ muffin : breakfast
- Ⓒ cereal : milk
- Ⓓ cheese : dairy

8. illness : recuperate ::
- Ⓐ emergency : hospital
- Ⓑ doctor : cure
- Ⓒ addiction : rehabilitate
- Ⓓ medicine : sickness

9. activity : toned ::
- Ⓐ sports : inactivity
- Ⓑ sports : athletes
- Ⓒ physical : mental
- Ⓓ inactivity : slack

10. fish : protein ::
- Ⓐ chicken : meat
- Ⓑ oil : fat
- Ⓒ egg : breakfast
- Ⓓ cauliflower : broccoli

11. inches : height ::
- Ⓐ growth : taller
- Ⓑ inches : measure
- Ⓒ pounds : weight
- Ⓓ pounds : scale

12. aspirin : fever ::
- Ⓐ feverish : hot
- Ⓑ headache : stress
- Ⓒ skin : clammy
- Ⓓ cast : broken bone

13. tear : ligament ::
- Ⓐ muscle : ache
- Ⓑ fracture : bone
- Ⓒ skin : covering
- Ⓓ elbow : joint

14. eyeglasses : vision ::
- Ⓐ braces : teeth
- Ⓑ floss : teeth
- Ⓒ brushing : gums
- Ⓓ nearsighted : farsighted

Analogy-Wiz

Write two analogies related to health. Leave off the last word. Trade analogies with a classmate to complete. When you are done, compare your answers.

_____

_____

Name _____ Date _____

Double-Word Search

(**Directions**) To complete this word search, first choose word pairs from the box to complete each analogy. Then, find the word pairs in the word search. They will be run together as one word and can run in any direction.

a. pulley : pull	**f.** brain : sensory	**k.** lawyer : courtroom
b. fulcrum : teeter-totter	**g.** bones : calcium	**l.** microwave oven : quick
c. sail : wind	**h.** distracted : attentive	**m.** student : civilian
d. facts : case	**i.** brick : mason	**n.** wool : sheep
e. curious : interested	**j.** cotton : fabric	**o.** sail : leisurely

```
d e b o r l i c r a n t a b i n o g r u s
r c a y l e r u s i e l l i a s a n d i h
l t c a w c a r s m o n n c m e y r n i o
o c o t o t o i c a t c i s i t a n b u n
s v e d o l r o i n e d e s c h o v e r i
m u f u l c r u m t e e t e r t o t t e r
b y r o s n e s n i a r b g o r a p a t s
b i s n h t s i e v e m n t w v i a r n t
s r i o e t s n i y o u i s a h a n e o a
q h a s e n o t y r y t h i v t y n e w b
i p a r p t m e i c u l a r e p d y o n i
m a m e r i b r i c k m a s o n v o g u l
n w h c a e e e l e o u n g v e o i n p u
s n f e s a c s t c a f f l e e y i n g n
d i s t r a c t e d a t t e n t i v e o f
y l a b u p u e t l i t l n q e r e h o o
x g s a y e i d e v i n c o u m e s o l r
t w l o s t u d e n t c i v i l i a n t c
b a r e e s u d r e r y s c c w h u c a e
r m o o l a n d i s t r i l k r a t s o g
```

1. smoker : slow :: _____

2. silk : silkworm :: _____

3. incline : ramp :: _____

4. clues : investigator :: _____

5. marine : military :: _____

6. bother : disturb :: _____

7. speedboat : rushed :: _____

8. heart : circulatory :: _____

9. word : writer :: _____

10. near : distant :: _____

Read All About It

To complete these analogies, you will need to supply the last word from words you already know to create two word pairs with similar relationships. The analogies in this exercise are all related in some way to reading.

Look at this example.

table of contents : front :: index : ?

Think: How does the first word pair relate? You find the table of contents in the front of a book. Where do you find the index?

Answer: The index is in the back of a book, so **back** completes this analogy.

(**Directions**) Read the first word pair, and decide how the two words are related. Then, complete the analogy with a word that gives the second word pair the same relationship. There may be more than one correct answer. Tell why the analogy works or what it is comparing. (For the example above, you could write "where parts of a book are found.")

1. unicorns : fantasy :: aliens : _____

_____

2. paragraph : chapter :: chapter : _____

_____

3. dictionary : words :: encyclopedia : _____

_____

4. glossary : definitions :: table of contents : _____

_____

5. novel : fiction :: biography : _____

_____

(GO ON ⇨)

Name _____ Date _____

Read All About It

Directions Read the first word pair, and decide how the two words are related. Then, complete the analogy with a word that gives the second word pair the same relationship. There may be more than one answer. Tell why the analogy works.

6. third-person : biography :: first-person : _____

_____

7. textbook : education :: comic book : _____

_____

8. thesaurus : synonym :: atlas : _____

_____

9. name : person :: title : _____

_____

10. love : romance novel :: crime : _____

_____

11. prose : novel :: verse : _____

_____

12. chapters : book :: acts : _____

_____

13. subjects : encyclopedia :: sites : _____

_____

14. lifelike qualities : personification :: exaggeration : _____

_____

Analogy-Wiz

Write three analogies that describe books you have read. The analogies should follow this example: Huck Finn : fiction :: Johnny Tremaine : historical fiction. Share your analogies with your class.

_____

_____

_____

Great Minds Think Alike

To complete these analogies, you will need to supply the last word from words you already know to create two word pairs with similar relationships. The analogies in this exercise are all related in some way to discoveries and inventions.

Look at this example.
Albert Einstein : atomic bomb :: Eli Whitney : ?

Think: How does the first word pair relate? Albert Einstein was instrumental in inventing the atomic bomb. What did Eli Whitney invent?

Answer: Eli Whitney invented the cotton gin, so **cotton gin** completes this analogy.

(**Directions**) Read the first word pair, and decide how the two words are related. Then, complete the analogy with a word that gives the second word pair the same relationship. There may be more than one correct answer. You may refer to resource books or the Internet for help finding the answers.

1. moveable type : printing :: wheel : _____

2. automobile : land travel :: boats : _____

3. sextant : GPS (Global Positioning System) :: typewriter : _____

4. Ferdinand Magellan : world :: Marco Polo : _____

5. modern medicine : health :: computers : _____

6. Alexander Graham Bell : telephone :: Samuel Morse : _____

(GO ON ⇒)

Great Minds Think Alike

(Directions) Read the first word pair, and decide how the two words are related. Then, complete the analogy with a word that gives the second word pair the same relationship. There may be more than one correct answer. You may refer to resource books or the Internet for help finding the answers.

7. Guglielmo Marconi : radio signals :: Elisha Otis : _____

8. biplane : jet :: Model-T : _____

9. Benjamin Franklin : electricity :: Louis Pasteur : _____

10. James Watt : steam engine :: Frank Whittle : _____

11. airplanes : Earth :: rockets : _____

12. electricity : domestic chores :: trains : _____

13. Wright brothers : flight :: Karl Benz : _____

14. Copernicus : solar system :: Magellan : _____

15. Johannes Kepler : planetary motion :: Isaac Newton : _____

16. Hans Lippershey : telescope :: Thomas Edison : _____

17. Ernest Rutherford : atom's nucleus :: Marie Curie : _____

18. Max Planck : quantum theory :: Albert Einstein : _____

Analogy-Wiz

Using the Internet and other resource materials, create a picture analogy about discovery or invention. Your pictures can be presented in any way you choose (as long as they are in the correct order of the analogy). Be creative! Display your pictorial analogies in your classroom.

All About Space

To complete these analogies, you will need to supply the second word from words you already know to create two word pairs with similar relationships. The analogies in this exercise are all related in some way to space.

Look at this example.
Earth : ? :: moon : Earth

Think: How does the second word pair relate? The moon orbits Earth. What does Earth orbit?

Answer: Earth orbits the sun, so **sun** completes this analogy.

(**Directions**) Read each analogy. Decide how the second word pair is related. Think of a word that relates to the first word in the same way. There may be more than one correct answer. Write your answer on the line. Write a brief explanation of why the analogy works.

1. rotate : _____ :: revolve : orbit

_____

2. astronomer : _____ :: geologist : rocks

_____

3. astronomy : _____ :: biology : microscope

_____

4. space : _____ :: Earth : gravity

_____

5. Earth : _____ :: Neptune : Pluto

_____

(GO ON ⇨)

All About Space

(Directions) Read each analogy. Decide how the second word pair is related. Think of a word or words that relate to the first word in the same way. There may be more than one correct answer. Write your answer on the line. Write a brief explanation of why the analogy works.

6. galaxy : _____ :: earth : solar system

_____

7. the distance light travels in a year : _____ :: 365 days : calendar year

_____

8. sun : _____ :: Earth : planet

_____

9. star : _____ :: firework : explosion

_____

10. star : _____ :: soldier : regiment

_____

11. orbit : _____ :: Earth : sphere

_____

12. Milky Way : _____ :: Mercury : planet

_____

13. moon : _____ :: sun : solar eclipse

_____

14. comet : _____ :: meteor : chunks of rock

_____

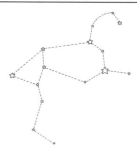

Analogy-Wiz

Look at a model of our solar system, and read about each planet. How many analogies can you make up about it? Think about sizes, distances from the sun, rings, moons, and temperatures. Share your analogies with your class.

Word(s) Up

> To complete these analogies, you will need to supply the second word from words you already know to create two word pairs with similar relationships. The analogies in this exercise are all related in some way to grammar.

Look at this example.

rigid : ? :: bendable : pliable

 Think: How does the second word pair relate? Bendable and pliable are synonyms. What is a synonym for rigid?

Answer: Stiff is one synonym for rigid, so **stiff** can complete this analogy.

(Directions) Read each analogy. Decide how the second word pair is related. Think of a word that relates to the first word in the same way. There may be more than one correct answer. Write your answer on the line. Write a brief explanation of why the analogy works.

1. unnerving : _____ :: general : specific

   _____

2. them : _____ :: us : we

   _____

3. distinguish : _____ :: slippery : slipperiest

   _____

4. they have : _____ :: can not : can't

   _____

5. turn : _____ :: pave : repaving

   _____

(GO ON ⇒)

Word(s) Up

(Directions) Read each analogy. Decide how the second word pair is related. Think of a word that relates to the first word in the same way. There may be more than one correct answer. Write your answer on the line. Write a brief explanation of why the analogy works.

6. groups : _____ :: thing : it

_____

7. drug : _____ :: piano : pianist

_____

8. go : _____ :: become : became

_____

9. discuss : _____ :: part : partition

_____

10. magnificent : _____ :: intelligent : intelligence

_____

11. maybe : _____ :: perhaps : surely

_____

12. depression : _____ :: decision : decide

_____

13. engage : _____ :: possess : dispossess

_____

14. sad : _____ :: happy : jubilant

_____

Analogy-Wiz

Write four grammar analogies. Then, erase the first word in one, the second word in one, the third word in one, and the fourth word in one. Trade analogies with a classmate to complete. Compare your answers.

_____

_____

_____

_____

Do Your Civic Duty

To complete these analogies, you will need to supply the third word from words you already know to create two word pairs with similar relationships. The analogies in this exercise are all related in some way to government and civics.

Look at this example.
president : United States :: _____ : state

Think: How does the first word pair relate? The president is the elected head of the United States. Who is the elected head of a state?

Answer: A governor is the elected head of a state, so **governor** completes this analogy.

Directions Read each analogy. Decide how the first word pair is related. Think of a word that relates to the last word in the same way. There may be more than one correct answer. You may use reference materials to help you. Write your answer on the line.

1. rules : family :: _____ : government

2. corporation : business :: _____ : state

3. takeover : business :: _____ : countries

4. parliament : England :: _____ : United States

5. mail : mailbox :: _____ : ballot box

6. spokesperson : group :: _____ : constituents

GO ON ⇨

Name _____   Date _____

Do Your Civic Duty

(Directions) Read each analogy. Decide how the first word pair is related. Think of a word that relates to the last word in the same way. There may be more than one correct answer. You may use reference materials to help you. Write your answer on the line.

7. communism : Cuba :: _____ : United States

8. representative : House :: _____ : Senate

9. partnerships : businesses :: _____ : governments

10. elected : president :: _____ : cabinet

11. contracts : businesses :: _____ : governments

12. donkey : Democratic Party :: _____ : Republican Party

13. mayor : city :: _____ : state

14. police force : local :: _____ : national

15. govern : rule :: _____ : ruler

16. vice-principal : school :: _____ : United States

17. fire : firefighters :: _____ : police officers

18. pass : approval :: _____ : disapproval

Analogy-Wiz

As a class, think of parallels between your town's government and your country's government. What comparisons can you make? What analogies can you create from your comparisons?

It's a Wonderful Life

To complete these analogies, you will need to supply the first word from words you already know to create two word pairs with similar relationships. The analogies in this exercise are all related in some way to life science.

Look at this example.

_____ : warm-blooded :: reptile : cold-blooded

Think: How does the second word pair relate? A reptile is cold-blooded; this is one of its characteristics. What animal group has the characteristic of being warm-blooded?

Answer: Mammals are warm-blooded, so **mammal** is a word that can complete this analogy.

Directions Read each analogy. Decide how the second word pair is related. Think of a word that relates to the second word in the same way. There may be more than one correct answer. Write your answer on the line.

1. _____ : birds :: scales : fish

2. _____ : amphibian :: live young : mammal

3. _____ : animal :: giant sequoia : tree

4. _____ : elephant :: saber-toothed cat : lion

5. _____ : herbivore :: meat : carnivore

6. _____ : whale :: hibernate : bear

GO ON ⇨

It's a Wonderful Life

Directions Read each analogy. Decide how the second word pair is related. Think of a word that relates to the second word in the same way. There may be more than one correct answer. Write your answer on the line.

7. _____ : threatened :: extinct : gone

8. _____ : preservation :: waste : shrinking resources

9. _____ : group :: animal : kingdom

10. _____ : internal skeleton :: invertebrate : exoskeleton

11. _____ : characteristics :: learning : habits

12. _____ : blink :: learned : scratch an itch

13. _____ : flower :: trunk : tree

14. _____ : photosynthesis :: water : growth

15. _____ : lady slippers :: cultivated : wheat

16. _____ : carrot :: leaves : lettuce

17. _____ : tomato :: vegetable : bean

18. _____ : maple tree :: evergreen : fir tree

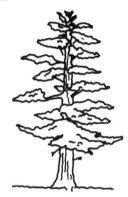

Analogy-Wiz

Write two analogies about life science, each on a different slip of paper. Leave the first word out of each one. Put your analogies together with the rest of your classmates' in a bowl or hat. Form two teams with the class. Take turns sending one team member up to the bowl to draw out an analogy and complete it. The team member may ask for help from one other teammate, and you can put a time limit on answers. Your team gets one point for each correct analogy. The team with the most points when the bowl is empty wins.

Name _____ Date _____

Do the Math

Directions Read each analogy. Decide how the second number pair is related. Think of a number that relates to the second number in the same way. Write your answer on the line. Write the calculation next to each problem, as is done with the first example. You may use a calculator.

1. 12 : 48 :: 11 : 44   _____ multiply by 4 _____

2. _____ : 20 :: 25 : 5   _____

3. _____ : 1 :: 50 : 100   _____

4. _____ : 49 :: 8 : 64   _____

5. _____ : 50 :: 50 : 500   _____

6. _____ : 78 :: 4 : 52   _____

7. _____ : 100 :: 4 : 400   _____

8. _____ : 12 :: 12 : 72   _____

9. _____ : –6 :: 18 : 0   _____

10. _____ : 12 :: 100 : 25   _____

11. _____ : 33 :: 100 : 300   _____

12. _____ : 86 :: 71 : 85   _____

13. _____ : –20 :: 40 : 20   _____

14. _____ : 36 :: 9 : 81   _____

15. _____ : 40 :: 39 : 63   _____

Analogies
Grades 6–8

Answer Key

page 3
C. forest
B. neck
A. brother
B. injure

pages 4–5
1. distant; antonyms
2. fryer; homophones
3. perish; rhymes
4. skill; synonyms
5. follow; antonyms
6. galaxy; parts of a whole
7. light; cause and effect
8. organs; parts of a group
9. desserts; parts of a group
10. shiver; cause and effect
11. shine; use
12. pound; use
13. play; use
14. clear; characteristic
15. silky; characteristic
16. taste; use
17. protect; use
18. temperature; use
19. dehydrate; characteristic
20. parch; characteristic
21. relax; use
22. identifying; use

pages 6–7
1. B; shapes
2. B; what they do
3. B; characteristic
4. A; characteristic
5. C; what they do
6. D; what they are made of
7. C; what they use at work
8. C; size
9. A; characteristic
10. B; state of preservation
11. B; add prefix "dis"
12. C; multiply by 5
13. B; superlatives
14. C; multiply by 3
15. B; extreme to mild
16. C; like pronouns
17. D; adjective to noun
18. A; divide by 4
19. B; add prefix "dis"
20. C; superlatives
21. B; add prefix "dis"

pages 8–9
Answers may vary.
1. melody; synonyms
2. girl; opposite sexes
3. snake; animal kingdoms
4. ants; how they live
5. seedling; growth sequence
6. build; what they do
7. checkers; what they are
8. drive; what we do with them
9. round; examples of
10. evening; sequence
11. game; what they are
12. axis; movement
13. lunar; how they are described
14. water; characteristics
15. predator; what they are
16. begin; synonyms
17. breathing; what they do
18. dribble, pass, or throw; how the ball is moved
19. words; what they contain
20. centimeters; parts
21. Earth; what revolves around each
22. bedroom; where we do things
23. giraffe; types of animals
24. camera; similar uses
25. rough; characteristics
26. hair; location of use
27. noise; antonyms
28. chair; things to sit on
29. sleigh; means of transportation
30. pull; synonyms

pages 10–11
1. athletic; antonyms
2. robust; synonyms
3. stutter; synonyms
4. rigid; antonyms
5. recollect; synonyms
6. arid; synonyms
7. cast aside; synonyms
8. fanciful; antonyms
9. dull; antonyms
10. justify; synonyms
11. soothe; synonyms
12. destroy; synonyms
13. state-of-the-art; antonyms
14. stilted; antonyms
15. happy; antonyms

pages 12–13
1. cloud; member of group
2. building; part to whole
3. grain; member of group
4. hobby; member of group
5. city; member of group
6. government; member of group
7. furniture; member of group
8. cat; member of group
9. ocean; member of group
10. toiletry; member of group
11. animal; member of group
12. arm; part to whole
13. Web site; part to whole
14. mail; part to whole
15. communication; member of group

pages 14–15
1. c.; cause/effect
2. d.; cause/effect
3. b.; effect/cause
4. a.; effect/cause
5. b. (or e.); cause/effect
6. f.; cause/effect
7. e. (or b.); effect/cause
8. h.; effect/cause
9. a.; cause/effect
10. j.; cause/effect
11. i.; effect/cause
12. c.; cause/effect
13. k.; cause/effect
14. g.; cause/effect
15. d.; effect/cause

pages 16–17
1. higher; homophone
2. delivering; grammar
3. noodle; rhyme
4. yours; grammar
5. twist; rhyme
6. presence; homophone
7. byway; rhyme
8. we're; grammar
9. demise; rhyme
10. chord; homophone
11. surround; rhyme
12. knight; homophone
13. businesses; grammar
14. rest; rhyme
15. reassess; grammar
16. relation; grammar

pages 18–19
1. illuminate; use
2. mathematician; who uses
3. historian; who uses
4. surgeon; what people do
5. air pressure; use
6. contain; use
7. comedian; what people do
8. musician; who uses
9. artist; who uses
10. writer; what people do
11. certify; use
12. support; use
Analogy-Wiz
1. a.; A dietitian works with food, and a biologist works with animals.
2. c.; An automobile is used for transportation, and a rollercoaster is used for entertainment.

pages 20–21
Wording may vary.
1. light; weight
2. amuse; what they do to us
3. capable; what each can do
4. solid; what each is like
5. entertaining; the use of each
6. narrow; size
7. predictable; what each is like
8. carnivore; what each eats
9. strength; what each needs most
10. strong; strength of each
11. uninhabited; numbers of people
12. abrasive; how each feels
Analogy-Wiz
1. a.; Each word pair describes how pliable a thing is.
2. c.; Each word pair describes a tiny part of a substance.

www.svschoolsupply.com
© Steck-Vaughn Company

Answer Key
Analogies 6–8, SV 6908-6

page 22
A. 1. speak, 2. actions,
3. than, 4. louder, 5. words;
B. 1. better, 2. two, 3. heads,
4. are, 5. one, 6. than

pages 23–24
1. C; how they move
2. A; what they travel
through
3. B; what makes each go
4. C; what moves each
5. D; what each is used for
6. A; speed
7. B; type of activity
8. D; where each is
9. B; who uses each
10. C; where each is used
11. A; purpose of each
12. B; characteristics of each
13. C; what steers each
14. C; who controls each
15. D; what controls traffic
of each

pages 25–26
1. B; how to score
2. A; what to hit with
3. C; where played
4. D; what to hit with
5. A; what matters most to
each
6. C; what matters most to
each
7. A; where each performs
8. C; how to catch ball for
each
9. D; where each takes place
10. A; what propels each
11. B; part of each
12. B; what each needs most
13. C; who uses each for
balance/support
14. C; who uses each for
protection

pages 27–28
1. B; what is used to make
each
2. C; synonyms
3. A; what each uses to put
image on
4. B; tool for each
5. D; purpose of each place
6. B; what each holds for
the artist
7. A; synonyms
8. C; types of paintings
9. A; how each is made
10. D; antonyms
11. C; how each is displayed
12. A; what can be made of
each
13. C; who is in charge of
each
14. B; parts of a whole
15. C; use of each tool

pages 29–30
1. B; opposite operations
2. C; what each measures
3. C; multiply by 3
4. A; characteristic of each
5. C; one-fourth of each
6. D; what each measures
7. A; number of sides
8. C; what results are called
9. D; units of each
10. B; how each angle
appears
11. D; comparable shapes
12. B; divide by 2
13. B; units of each
14. C; units of each
15. A; what results are called

pages 31–32
1. C; direction each is
measured in
2. A; climates of each
3. B; members of group
4. C; capitals of each
5. B; continent for each
6. D; where each is found
7. C; characteristic of each
8. A; direction of each on
globe
9. C; climate of each
10. A; where each is found
11. C; where each is found
12. D; members of group
13. A; ocean near each
14. B; capital of each
15. D; where each is found

pages 33–34
1. A; where each occurs
2. C; characteristic of each
3. B; what each studies
4. D; what each surrounds
5. C; where each is found
6. D; dangers of each
7. A; what each measures
8. B; how each is measured
9. C; how to describe each
10. D; characteristics
11. A; climate
12. C; typical precipitation
13. B; uses of each
14. B; worst of each
Analogy-Wiz
hailstorm : hail :: windstorm
: sand—what is blown
around in each
rain : drop :: snow : flake—
what each part is called
parka : snow : umbrella :
rain—gear for each
sprinkle : deluge :: flurry :
blizzard—worst of each

page 35
Answers are underlined.
1. fog, <u>drizzle</u>
2. <u>rainbow</u>, water
3. <u>them</u>, there
4. round, <u>geometry</u>
5. <u>competition</u>, improve
6. automobile, <u>highway</u>
7. <u>decrease</u>, separate
8. <u>your</u>, yours
9. <u>velocity</u>, light
10. eleven, <u>sixteen</u>
Bonus Analogy: <u>scramble</u>

pages 36–37
1. C; where each is worn
2. A; temperature and what
we wear
3. B; where shirt parts are
on body
4. C; what type of material
each is
5. A; how dressy each is
6. B; how each feels
7. A; type of each
8. B; apparel for each
activity
9. C; where each comes
from
10. B; colors of each

pages 38–39
1. B; characteristic
2. C; properties of each
3. B; opposites
4. A; example of each
5. C; opposite properties
6. A; how each is measured
7. B; force for each
8. A; how each is measured
9. C; result of each
10. B; what makes up each
11. A; temperatures of colors
12. B; effect of each
temperature
13. C; direction of each
force
14. A; freezing temperature
in each measurement
15. B; properties of each
16. B; charges of each

pages 40–41
1. D; verb to noun
2. B; verb to adjective
3. A; superlatives
4. C; verb to noun
5. B; synonyms
6. D; antonyms
7. A; verb to noun
8. D; synonyms
9. C; verb to noun
10. B; noun to adjective
11. D; noun to adjective
12. B; noun to adjective
13. A; synonyms
14. C; antonyms

pages 42–43
1. A; what is found in each
2. B; characteristics of each
3. C; shapes of each
4. A; temperatures of each
5. B; animal kingdoms
6. C; colors of each
7. D; sounds of each
8. A; uses for our bodies
9. C; how we view each
10. D; how each feels to us
11. B; qualities of each
12. C; ages of each
13. A; effect of each on us
14. C; effect of each on us
Analogy-Wiz
Answers may vary.
lace : fine :: burlap :
rugged—how each feels
porcelain : fragile :: steel :
strong—strength of each
rule : imperative ::
suggestion : optional—
how we view each
cloudy : overcast :: sunny :
bright—characteristics of
weather

Answer Key
Analogies 6–8, SV 6908-6

pages 44–45
1. C; job of each
2. B; subject of study
3. A; results of their work
4. C; group each leads
5. C; what each cares for
6. A; how each job is done
7. B; important final touch for each job
8. A; important quality for each job
9. C; important referral source for each job
10. B; who each needs most to succeed

Analogy-Wiz
Answers may vary.
canvas : artist :: paper : author—what they put their work on
surgeon : scalpel :: tailor : needle—tools they use
beach : lifeguard :: classroom : teacher—where each works
humor : comedian :: music : musician—what each creates

pages 46–47
1. D; how each is attended to
2. C; how our bodies use each
3. A; what they care for
4. A; important to each
5. B; how to improve each
6. C; similar results
7. D; food groups
8. C; how one improves
9. D; reaction of our muscles
10. B; food groups
11. C; units of measure
12. D; how we fix each
13. B; how each may be damaged
14. A; treatments for each

page 48
1. l.   6. e.
2. n.   7. o.
3. b.   8. f.
4. d.   9. i.
5. m.   10. h.

pages 49–50
Answers may vary.
1. science fiction; types of literature
2. book; parts of a whole
3. subjects; what each contains
4. chapters; what is found there
5. nonfiction; type of literature
6. autobiography; type of literature
7. entertainment; what each is used for
8. maps; what each is used for
9. book; similar uses
10. mystery; types of literature
11. poetry; types of writing
12. play; types of writing
13. Internet; how to use each
14. hyperbole; figurative language

pages 51–52
Answers may vary.
1. transportation; huge steps for each
2. water travel; what improved with each invention
3. word processor or computer; old method to new
4. China; where each explorer went
5. communication; made a huge impact on each
6. Morse code; their inventions
7. elevators (or the safety elevator); what they invented
8. race car; early prototypes of each
9. bacteria or pasteurization; what each discovered
10. jet engine; what each invented
11. space; where each travels
12. travel; each had huge impact
13. automobile; first flight and first automobile
14. world/Earth; each changed what people thought
15. gravity; each credited with theories
16. record player or electric light bulb; each made first
17. radium; discoveries
18. theory of relativity; discoveries

pages 53–54
Answers may vary.
1. axis; description of movement
2. space; what each studies
3. telescope; tools for each study
4. weightlessness; gravitational forces
5. Mars; next planet from sun
6. universe; parts of a whole
7. light year; definitions
8. star; what each is
9. supernova; both explosions
10. constellation; part of a whole
11. ellipse; shape of each
12. galaxy; what each is
13. lunar eclipse; similar occurrence for each
14. ice, dust, and gas; make-up of each

pages 55–56
Answers may vary.
1. calming; antonyms
2. they; object to subject pronouns
3. most distinguished; superlatives
4. they've; contractions
5. returning; add prefix "re" and suffix "ing"
6. they; pronoun for each
7. druggist; noun to person
8. went; past tense of each
9. discussion; verb to noun
10. magnificence; adjective to noun
11. probably; degrees of likelihood
12. depress; root words of each
13. disengage; add prefix "dis"
14. depressed; degrees of feeling

page 57
Answers may vary.
1. laws; what each makes
2. government; comparable decision-making bodies
3. war; comparable actions
4. congress; comparable government bodies
5. ballot; what goes in each box
6. politician; comparable political figure

page 58
7. democracy; types of government
8. senator; where each serves
9. alliances; comparable bonds
10. appointed; how they are chosen
11. treaties; official documents
12. elephant; mascot for each
13. governor; highest elected official of each
14. national guard; security forces for each
15. governor; verbs to nouns
16. vice-president; comparable government official
17. crime; what each fights
18. veto; action taken and result

pages 59–60
Answers may vary.
1. feathers; coverings
2. eggs; how they give birth
3. whale; largest in kingdom
4. wooly mammoth; ancestors of each
5. plant; what they eat
6. migrate; how they survive winter
7. endangered; synonyms
8. recycling; cause and effect
9. mammals; group to kingdom
10. vertebrate; definitions
11. genes; how we get each
12. involuntary action; why we do each
13. stem; comparable parts of each
14. sun; necessary to each process
15. wild; opposite types of growth
16. root; the part we eat
17. fruit; kind of food
18. deciduous; kind of leaves

page 61
2. 100; divide by 5
3. 2; multiply by 2
4. 7; multiply by itself
5. 5; multiply by 10
6. 6; multiply by 13
7. 1; multiply by 100
8. 2; multiply by 6
9. 12; subtract 18
10. 48; divide by 4
11. 11; multiply by 3
12. 72; add 14
13. 0; subtract 20; or add–40; divide by 2
14. 6; multiply by itself
15. 16; add 24